The Moon Landing

Kasia Reay

Illustrated by Colleen Larmour

Schofield & Sims

Mum was on night shift, so Nan was
with Mark for the week.

"Can we go to the m<u>oo</u>n ton<u>igh</u>t, Nan?" said M<u>ar</u>k.

"Yes," said Nan, "but we will n<u>ee</u>d a ro<u>ck</u>et, so go and get the junk bag."

Soon Nan had a ro<u>ck</u>et and M<u>ar</u>k had a jet-pa<u>ck</u>.

M<u>ar</u>k and Nan went into the <u>yar</u>d <u>for</u> lift o<u>ff</u>. 10, 9, 8, 7, 6, 5, 4, 3, 2, 1, lift o<u>ff</u>!

The rocket went BUMP in the thick moon dust. "You can go and look, but you must not go too far," said Nan.

So Mark set off. "Rocks and dust, just rocks and dust," he said to himself.

"Not <u>th</u>at <u>mu</u><u>ch</u> to s<u>ee</u>, Nan, so can we go ba<u>ck</u> n<u>ow</u>?" M<u>ar</u>k said.

"H<u>ow</u> was the m<u>oo</u>n land<u>ing</u>?"
said Mum the next m<u>or</u>n<u>ing</u>.

"Not bad, but I <u>th</u>ink M<u>ar</u>s mi<u>ght</u> be bett<u>er</u>," said M<u>ar</u>k. "Nan, can we go to M<u>ar</u>s?"

"Yes, in a ti_ck_," said Nan. "I just n_ee_d to h_oo_v_er_ up _th_is m_oo_n dust."